HYMNS AND CAROLS FOR CHRISTMAS

OXFORD UNIVERSITY PRESS

1984

Oxford University Press, Walton Street, Oxford OX2 6DP

London New York Toronto
Delhi Bombay Calcutta Madras Karachi
Kuala Lumpur Singapore Hong Kong Tokyo
Nairobi Dar es Salaam Cape Town
Melbourne Auckland
and associated companies in
Beirut Berlin Ibadan Mexico City Nicosia

Oxford is a trade mark of Oxford University Press

ISBN 0 19 143391 8

Printed in Great Britain
at the University Press, Oxford
by David Stanford
Printer to the University

FOREWORD

This collection of hymns and carols for the Christmas season is taken from the *Irish Church Hymnal*, and Oxford University Press is grateful to the General Synod of the Church of Ireland and to the Association for Promoting Christian Knowledge for allowing a selection to be made from their book and produced in this new form.

The traditional and long-established favourites which have enjoyed popularity for many years both in church services and in carol-singing events will be found in this compilation; in addition some less familiar texts, tunes, and alternative harmonizations have been included, and it is hoped that together they will provide an attractive choice of material for congregations and choirs during a season of the Christian calendar which will always make great demands on the repertoire of churches and choral groups who are seeking to enhance and enrich their Christmas celebrations.

Explanatory Note

The sign ⌣ at the end of a line is a phrasing mark, indicating that the next line should follow without a break, when practicable. This sign is intended chiefly for the use of choirs.

ACKNOWLEDGEMENTS

Oxford University Press wishes to thank the following who have given permission for copyright material to be included. Every effort has been made to trace copyright owners, and the compilers apologize to any whose rights have inadvertently not been acknowledged.

MUSIC

Composer/arranger	Copyright controlled by	Hymn No.
Davies, H. W.	Oxford University Press	28(2)
Evans, D.	Oxford University Press	10, from the *Revised Church Hymnary 1927*
Hewson, G. H. P.	Miss H. Hewson	4(1), 14, 23, 26(2), 40, 45(2)
Holst, G.	Oxford University Press	24, from the *English Hymnal*
Kitson, C. H.	APCK	7, 16, 45(1)
Pettman, E.	© Copyright 1961 B. Feldman & Co. Ltd., trading as H. Freeman & Co. Reproduced by permission of EMI Music Publishing Ltd. and International Music Publications	6(1), 22, 26(1), 35
Powell, F. J.	Composer	19
St. Patrick's Cathedral Dublin Collection		32, 34
Shaw, M.	A. R. Mowbray & Co. Ltd.	4(2) from the *English Carol Book*
	Oxford University Press	5(2), from the *Oxford Book of Carols*
	J. Curwen & Sons Ltd.	38
Vaughan Williams, R.	Oxford University Press	6(2), from *Enlarged Songs of Praise;* 28(1), from the *English Hymnal*
	Stainer & Bell Ltd.	30
Wilson, D. F. R.	Exors of Composer	8
Woodward, G. R.	Schott & Co. Ltd.	41

WORDS

Author/translator	Copyright controlled by	Hymn No.
Douglas, W.	© Church Pension Fund, USA	18, from *The Hymnal 1940*
Gillington, M. C.		32
The Hymnal 1940 (tr.)	© Church Pension Fund, USA	21
Lindsay, H. F. Selwood	Exors of Author	19
Pickard-Cambridge, W.		46
Woodward, G. R.	Schott & Co. Ltd.	41
	A. R. Mowbray & Co. Ltd.	42, from *The Cowley Carol Book*

1

DAVID GREGOR CORNER'S
Geistliche Nachtigall, Vienna, 1649.
Har. by CHARLES WOOD, 1866-1926

* This note is sometimes given as D natural.

Ein Kindlein in der Wiegen.

A BABE lies in the cradle,
A little babe so dear,
With noble light he shineth
As shines a mirror clear,
This little babe so dear.

2 The babe within the cradle
Is Jesus Christ our Lord;
To us all peace and amity
At this good time afford
Thou Jesus Christ our Lord.

3 Whoso would rock the cradle
Where lies the gentle child,
A lowly heart must lead him,
By passions undefiled,
As Mary pure and mild.

4 O Jesu, babe belovèd!
O Jesu, babe divine!
How mighty is thy wondrous love!
Fill thou this heart of mine
With that great love of thine.

German, 1649. Tr. *Paul England, d.* 1932

2

SANDYS

English Traditional Carol-Melody
from WILLIAM SANDYS'
Christmas Carols, London, 1833

A CHILD this day is born,
   A Child of high renown,
Most worthy of a sceptre,
   A sceptre and a crown:

> *Nowell, Nowell, Nowell,*
>   *Nowell, sing all we may,*
> *Because the King of all kings*ᴗ
>   *Was born this blessèd day.*

2 These tidings shepherds heard,
   In field watching their fold,
Were by an angel unto them
   That night revealed and told:

3 To whom the angel spoke,
   Saying, 'Be not afraid;
Be glad, poor silly* shepherds—
   Why are you so dismayed?

4 'For lo! I bring you tidingsᴗ
   Of gladness and of mirth,
Which cometh to all people byᴗ
   This holy Infant's birth':

5 Then was there with the angel
   An host incontinent*ᴗ
Of heavenly bright soldiers,
   Which from the highest was sent:

6 Lauding the Lord our God,
   And his celestial King;
All glory be in Paradise,
   This heavenly host did sing:

7 And as the angel told them,
   So to them did appear; [Christ,
They found the young Child, Jesus
   With Mary, his mother dear:

Traditional (English)

* silly = simple.

* incontinent = suddenly.

3

ES IST EIN' ROS'
ENTSPRUNGEN

76. 76. 676   German Traditional Carol Melody.
Harmonies based on MICHAEL PRAETORIUS' setting
in *Musae Sioniae*, Wolffenbüttel, 1609

A - men.

Μέγα καὶ παράδοξον θαῦμα.

A GREAT and mighty wonder,
A full and holy cure!
The Virgin bears the Infant
With virgin-honour pure.

Repeat the hymn again!
"To God on high be glory,
And peace on earth to men!"

2 The Word becomes incarnate
And yet remains on high!
The angel host sings anthems
To shepherds, from the sky.

3 Since all He comes to ransom,
By all be he adored,
The Infant born in Bethl'em
The Saviour and the Lord.   Amen.

Germanus, Patriarch of Constantinople, 635-733
Tr. *John M. Neale*, 1818-66, and others

3

A VIRGIN MOST PURE
(FIRST TUNE)

English Traditional Carol-Melody.
Arr. by GEORGE H. P. HEWSON, 1881-1972

A VIRGIN most pure, as the prophet foretold,
Should bring forth a Saviour whom now we behold;
To be our Redeemer from death, hell, and sin,
Which Adam's transgression had wrappèd us in:

Then let us be joyful, cast sorrow away,
Our Saviour Christ Jesus was born on this day.

2 In Bethlehem city, in Jewry, it was,
   That Joseph and Mary together did pass,
   All for to be taxèd when thither they came,
   For Caesar Augustus commanded the same:

3 But when they had entered the city so fair,
   A number of people so mighty was there,
   That Joseph and Mary, whose substance was small,
   Could find in the inn there no lodging at all:

4 There were they compelled in a stable to lie,
   Where the sheep and the oxen they usèd to tie;
   Their lodging so simple, they took it no scorn,
   But against the next morning the Saviour was born:

5 The King of all kings to this world being brought,
   Small store of fine linen to wrap him was sought,
   But when Mary had rockèd her young son so sweet,
   Within an ox manger she laid him to sleep:

6 To teach us humility all this was done,
   To learn us from thence haughty pride for to shun;
   The manger his cradle, who came from above,
   The great God of mercy, of peace, and of love:

                                        Traditional (English)

4

A VIRGIN MOST PURE
(SECOND TUNE)

English Traditional Carol-Melody
from DAVIES GILBERT'S
Some Ancient Christmas Carols, London, 1822,
as arr. by MARTIN F. E. SHAW, 1875-1958

A VIRGIN most pure, as the prophet foretold,
Should bring forth a Saviour whom now we behold;
To be our Redeemer from death, hell, and sin,
Which Adam's transgression had wrappèd us in:

Then let us be joyful, cast sorrow away,
Our Saviour Christ Jesus was born on this day.

2 In Bethlehem city, in Jewry, it was,
   That Joseph and Mary together did pass,
   All for to be taxèd when thither they came,
   For Caesar Augustus commanded the same:

3 But when they had entered the city so fair,
   A number of people so mighty was there,
   That Joseph and Mary, whose substance was small,
   Could find in the inn there no lodging at all:

4 There were they compelled in a stable to lie,
   Where the sheep and the oxen they usèd to tie;
   Their lodging so simple, they took it no scorn,
   But against the next morning the Saviour was born:

5 The King of all kings to this world being brought,
   Small store of fine linen to wrap him was sought,
   But when Mary had rockèd her young son so sweet,
   Within an ox manger she laid him to sleep:

6 To teach us humility all this was done,
   To learn us from thence haughty pride for to shun;
   The manger his cradle, who came from above,
   The great God of mercy, of peace, and of love:

                                Traditional (English)

7

5

WESTMINSTER ABBEY   87. 87. 87   Adapted from the Anthem
(FIRST TUNE)   "O God, thou art my God"
composed by HENRY PURCELL, 1659-95

A - men.

ANGELS, from the realms of glory,
　Wing your flight o'er all the earth;
Ye who sang creation's story
　Now proclaim Messiah's birth.
　　Come and worship,
　　Worship Christ, the new-born King!

2 Shepherds, in the field abiding,
　　Watching o'er your flocks by night,
　God with man is now residing,
　　Yonder shines the infant Light.

3 Sages, leave your contemplations,
　　Brighter visions gleam afar;
　Seek the great Desire of nations;
　　Ye have seen his natal star.

4 Saints, before the altar bending,
　　Watching long in hope and fear,
　Suddenly the Lord, descending,
　　In his temple shall appear.   Amen.

James Montgomery, 1771-1854

8

5 IRIS 8787 and refrain
(SECOND TUNE)

French Carol Melody,
harm. MARTIN SHAW, 1875–1958

REFRAIN

Come _____ and
Come _____ and

wor - ship (1st) Christ, the new - born King. ___
wor - ship (2nd) Wor - ship Christ, the new - born King.

9

6

NORMANDY
(FIRST TUNE)

Normandy Carol-Melody

AWAY in a manger, no crib for a bed,
The little Lord Jesus laid down his sweet head:
The stars in the bright sky looked down where he lay
The little Lord Jesus asleep on the hay.

2 The cattle are lowing, the Baby awakes,
But little Lord Jesus, no crying he makes.
I love thee, Lord Jesus! Look down from the sky,
And stay by my side until morning is nigh.

3 Be near me, Lord Jesus; I ask thee to stay
Close by me for ever, and love me, I pray.
Bless all the dear children in thy tender care,
And fit us for heaven, to live with thee there.

Anon., c. 1883

6

CRADLE SONG
(SECOND TUNE)

Melody by
WILLIAM J. KIRKPATRICK, 1838-1921.
Arr. by R. VAUGHAN WILLIAMS, 1872-1958

7

CHERRY TREE

English Traditional Carol-Melody.
Har. by CHARLES H. KITSON, 1874-1944

1. As Jo-seph was a walk-ing, He heard an an-gel sing,—
'This night shall be the birth-time Of Christ our heavenly King.'

CHORUS

'This night shall be the birth-time Of Christ our heavenly King.'

2 'He neither shall be born
   In housen nor in hall,
Nor in the place of Paradise,
   But in an ox's stall.'

3 'He neither shall be clothèd
   In purple nor in pall,
But in the pure white linen
   As usen babies all.'

4 'He neither shall be rockèd
   In silver nor in gold;
But in a wooden cradle
   That rocketh on the mould.'

5 As Joseph was a-walking,
   There did an Angel sing,
And Mary's Child at midnight
   Was born to be our King.

6 Then be ye glad, good people,
   This night of all the year,
And lift your hearts in joyfulness,
   His star it shineth clear.

Traditional (English)

8

TYHOLLAND   777   German Traditional Carol Melody.
Adapted by the Very Rev. DAVID FREDERICK RUDDELL WILSON, 1871-1957

A - men.

BLESSED night, when first that plain
Echoed with the joyful strain:
'Peace has come to earth again.'

2 Happy shepherds, on whose ear
Fell the tidings glad and dear;
'God to man is drawing near.'

3 Babe of promise, born at last,
After weary ages past,
When our hopes were overcast,

4 We adore thee as our King,
And to thee our song we sing,
Our best offering to thee bring.

5 'Lamb of God'—thy lowly Name,
King of kings we thee proclaim,
Heaven and earth shall hear its fame.   Amen.

Horatius Bonar, 1808-89

13

9

LUTHER (NUN FREUT EUCH)   87. 87. 887   Later form of a melody
in JOSEPH KLUG'S *Geistliche Lieder*, Wittemberg, 1535.
Arr. and har. by JOHANN SEBASTIAN BACH, 1685-1750

Ich steh an deiner Krippen hier.

BESIDE thy cradle here I stand,
 O thou that ever livest,
And bring thee with a willing hand
 The very gifts thou givest.
Accept me; 'tis my mind, my heart,
My soul, my strength, my ev'ry part,
 That thou from me requirest.

Paul Gerhardt, 1607-76.
Tr. *John Troutbeck*, 1832-99

14

9

LUTHER (NUN FREUT EUCH)   87. 87. 887   Later form of a melody
(Simpler form)   in JOSEPH KLUG's *Geistliche Lieder*, Wittemberg, 1535

Ich steh an deiner Krippen hier.

BESIDE thy cradle here I stand,
O thou that ever livest,
And bring thee with a willing hand
The very gifts thou givest.
Accept me; 'tis my mind, my heart,
My soul, my strength, my ev'ry part,
That thou from me requirest.

Paul Gerhardt, 1607-76.
Tr. *John Troutbeck*, 1832-99

15

BUNESSAN
UNISON

55. 53. D

Gaelic Melody.
Arr. by DAVID EVANS, 1874-1948

A - men.

Leanabh an Aigh.

CHILD in the manger,
  Infant of Mary;
Outcast and stranger,
  Lord of all!
Child who inherits
  All our transgressions,
All our demerits
  On him fall.

2 Once the most holy
    Child of salvation,
  Gentle and lowly,
    Livèd below;
  Now, as our glorious
    Mighty Redeemer,
  See him victorious
    O'er each foe.

3 Prophets foretold him,
    Infant of wonder;
  Angels behold him
    On his throne;
  Worthy our Saviour
    Of all their praises;
  Happy for ever
    Are his own.   Amen.

Mary MacDonald, 1817-c. 1890
Tr. *Lachlan MacBean, 1853-1931*

16

11

DANS CETTE ÉTABLE

French Carol-Melody (18th cent.).
Set by CHARLES FRANÇOIS GOUNOD, 1818-93

1. Cra-dled all low-ly, Be-hold the Sa-viour Child! A Be-ing ho-ly, In dwell-ing rude and wild;— Ne'er yet was re-gal state Of mon-arch proud and great, Who grasped a na-tion's fate,— So glo-rious as the man-ger-bed of Beth-le - hem.

2 No longer sorrow
   As without hope, O earth!
A brighter morrow
   Dawned with that Infant's birth.
Our sins were great and sore,
But these the Saviour bore,
And God was wroth no more:
His own Son was the Child that
   lay in Bethlehem.

3 Babe weak and wailing,
   In lowly village stall
Thy glory veiling,
   Thou cam'st to die for all.
The sacrifice is done,
The world's atonement won,
Till time its course hath run,
O Jesus, Saviour, Morning Star
   of Bethlehem.

H. B. Farnie, 1837-89

12

10. 10. 10. 10. 10. 10   Melody (slightly altered) by
JOHN WAINWRIGHT, 1723-68

A - men.

CHRISTIANS, awake, salute the happy morn,
Whereon the Saviour of the world was born;
Rise to adore the mystery of love,
Which hosts of angels chanted from above;
With them the joyful tidings first begun
Of God incarnate and the Virgin's Son.

2 Then to the watchful shepherds it was told,
  Who heard the angelic herald's voice: 'Behold,
  I bring good tidings of a Saviour's birth
  To you and all the nations upon earth:
  This day hath God fulfilled his promised word,
  This day is born a Saviour, Christ the Lord.'

3 He spake; and straightway the celestial choir
  In hymns of joy, unknown before, conspire:
  The praises of redeeming love they sang,
  And heaven's whole orb with hallelujahs rang;
  God's highest glory was their anthem still,
  Peace upon earth, and unto men good-will.   Amen.

John Byrom, 1691-1763

13

BRANLE DE L'OFFICIAL

THOINOT ARBEAU'S
Orchésographie, Langres, 1588.
Har. by CHARLES WOOD, 1866-1926

1. Ding dong! mer-ri-ly on high   In heaven the bells are ring-ing:
   Ding dong! ver-i-ly the sky   Is riv'n with an-gel sing-ing:

2. E'en so here be-low, be-low,   Let stee-ple bells be swung-en,
   And *i - o, i - o, i - o,   By priests and peo-ple sung-en:

3. Pray you, du-ti-ful-ly prime Your Mat - in chime, ye ring-ers;
   May you beau-ti-ful-ly rime Your Eve-time Song, ye sing-ers:

Glo - ri - a, Ho - san - na in ex - cel - sis!

* Io is an expression of joy.

George R. Woodward, 1848-1934

14

EARTH TO-DAY REJOICES — Melody from *Piae Cantiones*, Greifswald, 1582.
Har. by GEORGE H. P. HEWSON, 1881-1972

With vigour, in quick time

1. Earth to-day re - joi - ces,
And ce - les-tial voi - ces,
2. Re - con - ci - li - a - tion,
Glad-ness and sal - va - tion,

Hal-le - lu - jah! Hal-le - lu - jah!

Hal - le - lu - jah!

Death can hurt no more;
Tell the ti - dings o'er.
Peace has came for aye;
Came on Christ-mas Day.

Now let strife and dis-cord cease, Now to man has come our peace.

rall.

Hal - le - lu - jah! Hal-le - lu - jah!

Based on *John M. Neale*, 1818-66

15

PUER NOBIS NASCITUR
UNISON

L.M.   German Traditional Carol Melody,
as adapted in MICHAEL PRAETORIUS'
Musae Sioniae, Wolffenbüttel, 1609

A - men.

A solis ortus cardine.

f   FROM east to west, from shore to shore,
Let every heart awake and sing
The holy Child whom Mary bore,
The Christ, the everlasting King.

22

mf 2 Behold, the world's Creator wears·
    The form and fashion of a slave;
    Our very flesh our Maker shares,
    His fallen creature, man, to save.

3 For this how wondrously he wrought!
    A maiden, in her lowly place,
    Became, in ways beyond all thought,
    The chosen vessel of his grace.

4 He shrank not from the oxen's stall,
    He lay within the manger bed,
    And he, whose bounty feedeth all,
    At Mary's breast himself was fed.

cresc 5 And while the angels in the sky
    Sang praise above the silent field,
    To shepherds poor the Lord most high,
    The one great Shepherd, was revealed.

6 All glory for this blessèd morn
    To God the Father ever be;
    All praise to thee, O Virgin-born,
    All praise O Holy Ghost, to thee.   Amen.

Coelius Sedulius, c. 450. Tr. *John Ellerton,* 1826-93

16

GOD REST YOU MERRY

English Traditional Carol-Melody.
Har. by CHARLES H. KITSON, 1874-1944

1. God rest you mer-ry, gen-tle-men, Let no-thing you dis - may,

For Je - sus Christ our Sa - viour Was born up - on this day,

To save us all from Sa-tan's power When we had gone a - stray.

CHORUS

O ti - dings of com - fort and joy, com-fort and

joy, O___ ti - dings of com - fort and joy!

24

2 From God our Heavenly Father
  A blessèd angel came;
  And unto certain shepherds
  Brought tidings of the same;
  How that in Bethlehem was born
  The Son of God by name:

3 The shepherds at those tidings
  Rejoicèd much in mind,
  And left their flocks a-feeding
  In tempest, storm, and wind;
  And went to Bethlehem straightway,
  This blessèd Babe to find:

4 But when to Bethlehem they came,
  Whereat this infant lay,
  They found him in a manger,
  Where oxen feed on hay;
  His mother Mary, kneeling down,
  Unto her Lord did pray:

.5 Now to the Lord sing praises,
  All you within this place;
  And with true love and brotherhood
  Each other now embrace.
  This holy tide of Christmas
  All others doth efface:

Traditional (English)

17

GOOD CHRISTIAN MEN, REJOICE
(IN DULCI JUBILO)

Later form of a
German Carol-Melody (14th cent.).
Har. by ROBERT LUCAS DE PEARSALL, 1795-1856

1. Good Chris - tian men, re - joice_____ With heart, and
soul, and voice;_____ Give ye heed to what we

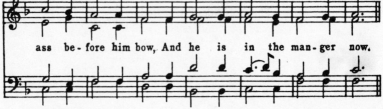

say; Je - sus Christ is born to - day; Ox and
ass be - fore him bow, And he is in the man - ger now.

Christ is born to-day,_____ Christ is born to-day!

2 Good Christian men, rejoice
   With heart, and soul, and voice;
      Now ye hear of endless bliss:
      Jesus Christ was born for this;
   He hath oped the heavenly door,
   And man is blessed evermore.
         Christ was born for this!

3 Good Christian men, rejoice
   With heart, and soul, and voice;
      Now ye need not fear the grave:
      Jesus Christ was born to save:
   Calls you one, and calls you all,
   To gain his everlasting hall.
         Christ was born to save!

                    John M. Neale, 1818-66

18

FROM HIGHEST HEAVEN   L.M.   Later form of a melody
(VOM HIMMEL HOCH)   in VALENTIN SCHUMANN'S *Geistliche Lieder*, Leipzig, 1539

A-men.

Vom Himmel hoch da komm ich her.

The Angel's Message

'FROM heaven high I come to you,
I bring you tidings good and new,
Good tidings of great joy I bring:
Thereof will I both say and sing:

2 'For you a little Child is born
Of God's own chosen maid, this morn:
A fair and tender baby bright,
To be your joy and your delight.

3 'Lo, he is Christ, the Lord indeed,
Our God, to guide you in your need:
And he will be your Saviour, strong،
To cleanse you from all sin and wrong.'

Our Response

4 Now let us all right merry be,
And, with the shepherds, go to see،
God's own dear Son, within the stall;
His gift, bestowed upon us all.

5 Mark well, my heart; look well, mine eyes;
Who is it in the manger lies:
What child is this, so young and
It is my Jesus lieth there.   [fair?

p 6 Ah! dearest Jesus, holy Child,
Make thee a bed, soft, undefiled,
Within my heart, and there recline,
And keep that chamber ever thine.   Amen.

Martin Luther, 1483-1546
Tr. *Winfred Douglas, 1867-1944*

28

19

CASTLEMARTYR

Rev. Frederick James Powell, 1894-

HUSH thee to sleep,
Sweet thy repose,
Let thy baby eyes tenderly close;
Angels above thee
Watch o'er thy bed,
Watch o'er the Christ-Child in Mary's arms laid.

2 Whom seers foretold
Angels unfold,
Wondering shepherds with trembling behold;
Magi adore him
Round that rude bed,
Worship the Christ-Child in Mary's arms laid.

3 Oxen and sheep
Low there and bleat,
Gifts are laid at the young Child's feet;
Gold for a kingdom,
Myrrh for his grave,
Incense, the Lord Christ in Mary's arms laid.

H. F. Selwood Lindsay, 1903-72

20

CHRISTMAS (MENDELSSOHN) 77. 77. D, and Refrain

Adapted by
WILLIAM HAYMAN CUMMINGS, 1831-1915,
from a chorus in J. L. FELIX MENDELSSOHN-BARTHOLDY's *Festgesang*

Org. Ped.

HARK! the herald-angels sing
Glory to the new-born King;
Peace on earth, and mercy mild,
God and sinners reconciled!
Joyful, all ye nations, rise,
Join the triumph of the skies;
With the angelic host proclaim,
Christ is born in Bethlehem.

Hark! the herald-angels sing
Glory to the new-born King.

2 Christ, by highest heaven adored!
Christ, the everlasting Lord!
Late in time behold him come,
Offspring of a Virgin's womb.
Veiled in flesh the Godhead see;
Hail, the incarnate Deity,
Pleased as Man with men to dwell,
Jesus, our Emmanuel.

3 Hail, the heaven-born Prince of peace!
Hail, the Sun of righteousness!
Light and life to all he brings,
Risen with healing in his wings.
Mild, he lays his glory by,
Born that man no more may die,
Born to raise the sons of earth,
Born to give them second birth.

Charles Wesley, 1707-88, and others

21

ES IST EIN' ROS' ENTSPRUNGEN

German Traditional Carol-Melody.
Adapted and har. by
MICHAEL PRAETORIUS, 1571-1621

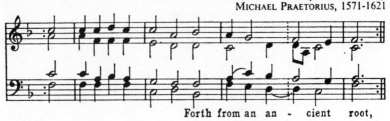

Forth from an an - cient root,

When half-spent was the night.

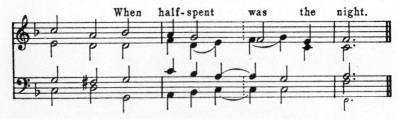

[*The barring of this tune is necessarily irregular; but its performance will be found to be easy if it is remembered that the time-value of a crotchet is the same throughout.*]

Es ist ein' Ros' entsprungen.

I KNOW a rose-tree springing
Forth from an ancient root,
As men of old were singing.
From Jesse came the shoot
That bore a blossom bright
Amid the cold of winter,
When half-spent was the night.

2 This rose-tree, blossom-laden,
  Whereof Isaiah spake,
Is Mary, peerless maiden,
  Who mothered, for our sake,
  The little Child, new-born
By God's eternal counsel
  On that first Christmas morn.

3 O Flower, whose fragrance tender
  With sweetness fills the air,
Dispel in glorious splendour
  The darkness ev'rywhere;
  True man, yet very God,
From sin and death now save us,
  And share our every load.

Spierischen Gesangbuch
The Hymnal (1940) *U.S.A.*

32

22

I SAW A MAIDEN

Old Basque Noël.
Arr., with refrain added, by EDGAR PETTMAN, 1865-1943

1. I saw a mai-den sit-ting and sing, She lull'd her Child a lit-tle Lord - ing. Lul - lay, ___ Lul - lay, ___ my ___ dear Son, my sweet-ing, Lul - lay, ___ Lul - lay, my dear Son, my own dear dear - ing.

REFRAIN

poco rall. e dim.

2 This very Lord, he made all things,
   And this very God, the King of all kings.

3 There was sweet music at this Child's birth,
   And heaven fill'd with angels making much mirth.

4 Heaven's angels sang to welcome the Child
   Now born of a maid, all undefiled.

5 Pray we and sing on this festal day:
   That peace may dwell with us alway.

15th cent. words from the Sloane MSS.

33

23

IN SORROW AND IN WANT
(ALL IN A GARDEN GREEN)

Melody from WILL BALLET'S *MS. Lute Book*,
c. 1600, in the Library of Trinity College, Dublin.
Har. by GEORGE H. P. HEWSON, 1881-1972

1. In sor-row and in want, a-mid the win-ter wild, The
Mo-ther-Maid in Bethlehem's inn brought forth her first-born Child:

CHORUS

Re-joice, ye hum-ble souls, sing songs up-on your way; With
heart and voice re-joice, re-joice, With heart and voice re-
joice, re-joice; your Lord is born to-day.

2 He came with royal grace, his choicest gifts to give;
  In tenderness of love he came to teach our souls to live:

3 He came in lowly grief to suffer and to die,
  That we might rise from death and sin to live with him on high:

4 For him the shepherd band have left their lonely fold;
  The star-led worshippers for him bring incense, myrrh, and gold:

5 For him the midnight skies flash forth with angel wings;
  That little Babe in manger laid, he is the King of kings:

From *Frederick W. Farrar*, 1831-1903

24

CRANHAM   Irregular   GUSTAV THEODORE HOLST,
1874-1934

1.   In   the bleak mid - win - ter
2. Our   God, heaven can - not   hold   him,
3. E - nough   for him, whom Cher - u - bim
4.   An - gels and arch - an - gels
5.   What   can   I   give   him,

Fros - ty wind made   moan, —   Earth stood hard as
Nor   earth sus - tain; —   Heaven and earth shall
Wor - ship night and   day, —   A   breast - ful of
May have ga - thered there, —   Cher - u - bim and
Poor   as I   am? —   If   I were a

    i - ron,   Wa - ter like   a   stone:
flee   a - way   When he comes   to   reign:
milk   And a   man - ger - ful of   hay;
ser - a - phim   Thronged   the   air —
shep - herd,   I   would bring   a   lamb,

Snow had fall - en, snow on snow,—
In the bleak mid - win - ter A
E - nough for him, whom an - gels—
But on - - ly his mo - ther—
If I were a wise— man—

Snow— on— snow, In the bleak mid -
sta - ble place suf - ficed The Lord— God Al -
Fall— down be - fore, The ox and ass and
In her mai - den bliss Wor- shipped the Be -
I would do my part; Yet what I can I

win - ter, Long— a - - go.
might - y Je - sus— Christ.
cam - el Which— a - - dore.
lov - ed With— a— kiss.
give him— Give— my— heart.

Christina G. Rossetti, 1830-94

37

25

NOEL
(FIRST TUNE)

D.C.M.   English Traditional Melody.
Adapted by SIR ARTHUR SEYMOUR SULLIVAN, 1842-1900.
(Last four lines added by the adapter)

A - men.

25

ST. SILVESTER
(SECOND TUNE)

D.C.M.   SIR JOSEPH BARNBY, 1838-96

A-men.

IT came upon the midnight clear,
   That glorious song of old,
From angels bending near the earth
   To touch their harps of gold:
'Peace on the earth, good-will to
               [men,
   From heaven's all-gracious King!'
The world in solemn stillness lay
   To hear the angels sing.

2 Still through the cloven skies they
               [come,
   With peaceful wings unfurled;
And still their heavenly music floats
   O'er all the weary world;
Above its sad and lowly plains
   They bend on hovering wing;
And ever o'er its Babel-sounds
   The blessèd angels sing.

3 Yet with the woes of sin and strife
   The world has suffered long;
Beneath the angel-strain have rolled
   Two thousand years of wrong;
And man, at war with man, hears not
   The words of peace they bring:
O listen now, ye men of strife,
   And hear the angels sing!

4 For lo! the days are hastening on,
   By prophet-bards foretold,
When, with the ever-circling years,
   Comes round the age of gold:
When peace shall over all the earth
   Its ancient splendours fling,
And the whole world give back the song
   Which now the angels sing. Amen.

Edmund H. Sears, 1821-76

26

LOVE came down at Christmas,
   Love all lovely, Love divine;
Love was born at Christmas,
   Star and angels gave the sign.

2 Worship we the Godhead,
   Love incarnate, Love divine;
Worship we our Jesus:
   But wherewith for sacred sign?

3 Love shall be our token,
   Love be yours and love be mine,
Love to God and all men,
   Love for plea and gift and sign.

Christina G. Rossetti, 1830-94

26

GARTAN
(SECOND TUNE)

67. 67   Irish Traditional Hymn Melody.
Har. by GEORGE HENRY PHILLIPS HEWSON, 1881-1972

LOVE came down at Christmas,
   Love all lovely, Love divine;
Love was born at Christmas,
   Star and angels gave the sign.

2 Worship we the Godhead,
   Love incarnate, Love divine;
Worship we our Jesus:
   But wherewith for sacred sign?

3 Love shall be our token,
   Love be yours and love be mine,
Love to God and all men,
   Love for plea and gift and sign.

Christina G. Rossetti, 1830-94

41

27 (i)

ADESTE FIDELES　　　　Irregular　　　　Melody by
JOHN FRANCIS WADE (?),
c. 1710 or 1711-86

Adeste fideles

O COME, all ye faithful,
Joyful and triumphant,
O come ye, O come ye to Bethlehem;
Come and behold him
Born the King of angels;
O come, let us adore him,
O come, let us adore him,
O come, let us adore him, Christ the Lord.

2   God of God,
Light of Light,
Lo! he abhors not the Virgin's womb;
Very God,
Begotten, not created;

3   Sing, choirs of angels,
Sing in exultation,
Sing, all ye citizens of heaven above,
'Glory to God
In the highest':

For Christmas Day

4   Yea, Lord, we greet thee,
Born this happy morning;
Jesus, to thee be glory given:
Word of the Father,
Now in flesh appearing;

Possibly by John Wade, c. 1711–86
Tr. Frederick Oakeley, 1802–80, and others

ADESTE FIDELES   Irregular   Melody by
JOHN FRANCIS WADE (?),
c. 1710 or 1711-86

(*a*) Use in Verse 1 only.   (*b*) Omit in verses 2, 3, 4 and 5.

Adeste, fideles.

O COME, all ye faithful,
Joyful and triumphant;
To Bethlehem hasten now with glad accord;
Come and behold him,
Born, the King of angels:
O come, let us adore him, Christ the Lord.

2   Sing, choirs of angels,
Sing in exultation,
Thro' heaven's high arches be your praises poured;
Now to our God be,
Glory in the highest:

3   See how the shepherds,
Summoned to his cradle,
Leaving their flocks, draw nigh with lowly fear;
We too will thither,
Bend our joyful footsteps:

4   Lo! star-led chieftains,
Magi, Christ adoring,
Offer him frankincense, and gold and myrrh;
We to the Christ-child
Bring our hearts' oblations:

5   Yea, Lord, we bless thee,
Born for our salvation;
Jesu! for ever be thy Name adored!
Word of the Father,
Now in flesh appearing:

Latin, 18th cent. Tr. *Frederick Oakeley*, 1802-80
and others

28

FOREST GREEN
(FIRST TUNE)

D.C.M. (Irregular) English Traditional Melody.
Adapted and har. by
RALPH VAUGHAN WILLIAMS, 1872-1958

A - men.

28

CHRISTMAS CAROL
(SECOND TUNE)

D.C.M. (Irregular) SIR HENRY WALFORD DAVIES,
1869-1941

A - men.

mp O LITTLE town of Bethlehem,
　How still we see thee lie!
Above thy deep and dreamless sleep
　The silent stars go by;
Yet in thy dark streets shineth
　The everlasting Light;
The hopes and fears of all the years
　Are met in thee tonight.

2 For Christ is born of Mary;
　And, gathered all above,
While mortals sleep, the angels keep
　Their watch of wondering love.
O morning stars, together
　Proclaim the holy birth,
And praises sing to God the King,
　And peace to men on earth.

3 How silently, how silently,
　The wondrous gift is given!
So God imparts to human hearts
　The blessings of his heaven.
No ear may hear his coming;
　But in this world of sin,
Where meek souls will receive him, still
　The dear Christ enters in.

4 O holy Child of Bethlehem,
　Descend to us, we pray;
Cast out our sin, and enter in;
　Be born in us today.
cresc. We hear the Christmas angels
　The great glad tidings tell;
O come to us, abide with us,
　Our Lord Emmanuel.　Amen.

Bishop Phillips Brooks, 1835-93

29

CORDE NATUS EX PARENTIS 87. 87. 877   Mediæval Melody.
(DIVINUM MYSTERIUM)   *Piae Cantiones* (THEODORIC PETRI of Nyland),
UNISON   Greifswald, 1582

A - men.

Corde natus ex Parentis.

OF the Father's love begotten
　　Ere the worlds began to be,
He is Alpha, he is Omega,
　　He the source, the ending he,
Of the things that are, that have been,
　　And that future years shall see,
　　　Evermore and evermore.

2 O that birth for ever blessèd!
　　When the Virgin full of grace,
By the Holy Ghost conceiving,
　　Bare the Saviour of our race,
And the Babe, the world's Redeemer,
　　First revealed his sacred face,
　　　Evermore and evermore.

3 This is he whom seers and sages
　　Sang of old with one accord;
Whom the writings of the prophets
　　Promised in their faithful word;
Now he shines, the long-expected:
　　Let creation praise its Lord,
　　　Evermore and evermore.

4 O ye heights of heaven, adore him;
　　Angel-hosts, his praises sing;
Powers, dominions, bow before him,
　　And extol our God and King:
Let no tongue on earth be silent,
　　Every voice in concert ring,
　　　Evermore and evermore.

5 Christ, to thee, with God the Father,
　　And, O Holy Ghost, to thee,
Hymn and chant and high thanksgiving
　　And unwearied praises be,
Honour, glory, and dominion,
　　And eternal victory,
　　　Evermore and evermore.　Amen.

Aurelius Clemens Prudentius, c. 348-413
Tr. *John M. Neale*, 1818-66, *Sir Henry W. Baker*,
　　　　　　　　　1821-77, and others

30

SUSSEX CAROL

English Traditional Carol-Melody.
Arr. by R. Vaughan Williams, 1872-1958

Verses 1, 2 & 4

On Christ-mas night all Christians sing, To hear the news the an - gels bring. On Christ-mas night all Christians sing, To hear the news the an - gels bring- News of great joy, news of great mirth, News of our mer - ci - ful King's birth.

2 Then why should men on earth be so sad,
  Since our Redeemer made us glad,
  When from our sin he set us free,
  All for to gain our liberty.

4 All out of darkness we have light,
  Which made the angels sing this night;
  'Glory to God and peace to men,
  Now and for evermore.   Amen.'

Traditional (English)

Verse 3

When sin de-parts be - fore his

When sin de-parts be-fore his grace, Then life and health come

grace,_____ When sin de-parts be - fore_ his grace, Then

grace, Then life and health come_

in its place, Then life and health come_

grace, Then_ life and health come

life and health come in its place; An-gels and men with joy_ may

in its place;_____ An-gels_____ may

in its place;_____ An-gels_____ may

sing,_ All for to see the new-born King.

IRBY 87. 87. 77 Melody by
HENRY JOHN GAUNTLETT, 1805-76

ONCE in royal David's city
　Stood a lowly cattle shed,
Where a mother laid her baby
　In a manger for his bed;
Mary was that mother mild,
Jesus Christ her little child.

2 He came down to earth from heaven
　　Who is God and Lord of all,
　And his shelter was a stable,
　　And his cradle was a stall;
　With the poor and mean and lowly
　Lived on earth our Saviour holy.

3 And through all his wondrous childhood,
    He would honour and obey,
Love and watch the lowly mother
    In whose gentle arms he lay;
Christian children all must beʋ
Mild, obedient, good as he.

4 For he is our childhood's pattern,
    Day by day, like us, he grew;
He was little, weak, and helpless,
    Tears and smiles like us he knew;
And he feeleth for our sadness,
And he shareth in our gladness.

5 And our eyes at last shall see him,
    Through his own redeeming love,
For that Child so dear and gentle
    Is our Lord in heaven above;
And he leads his children on
To the place where he is gone.

6 Not in that poor lowly stable,
    With the oxen standing by,
We shall see him; but in heaven,
    Set at God's right hand on high;
When like stars his children crowned
All in white shall wait around.

Mrs. Cecil F. Alexander, 1818-95

32

OVER THE HILLS

Norwegian Melody.
Setting from the Collection at
St. Patrick's Cathedral, Dublin

After last verse

O - ver the hills, o - ver the snow.

Organ

OVER the hills, and over the vales,
Over the fields of snow,
The Christ-Child came and brought for me
A golden shining Christmas tree—
It was a Cross, whereon did grow
All happy things the world can know.

2 Over the hills, and over the vales,
  Over the fields of snow,
  The Christ-Child came and brought for me,
  A little bed so fair to see—
  It was a manger poor and bare,
  But sweet and holy thoughts were there.

3 Over the hills, and over the vales,
  Over the fields of snow,
  The Christ-Child came and brought for me
  A Christmas gift, the best might be:
  O beauteous gift! It was the Love
  That brought him here from heaven above.

4 Over the hills, and over the vales,
  Over the fields of snow,
  The Christ-Child wanders for my sake—
  And there will I my pathway take,
  And there unto my Lord and King
  My heart and worship will I bring.
    Over the hills, over the snow.

M. C. Gillington

55

HUMILITY   SIR JOHN GOSS, 1800-80

UNISON

See a-mid the win-ter's snow, Born for us on earth be-low;

See the ten-der Lamb ap-pears, Prom-ised from e - ter-nal years:

HARMONY

Hail, thou e - ver-bless-ed morn; Hail, re-demption's hap-py dawn;

Sing through all Je - ru - sa - lem, Christ is born in Beth-le-hem.

2 Lo, within a manger lies
   He who built the starry skies;
   He who throned in height sublime
   Sits amid the cherubim!

3 Say, ye holy shepherds, say
   What your joyful news to-day;
   Wherefore have ye left your sheep
   On the lonely mountain steep?

4 'As we watched at dead of night,
   Lo, we saw a wondrous light;
   Angels singing "Peace on earth"
   Told us of the Saviour's birth':

5 Sacred Infant, all divine,
   What a tender love was thine,
   Thus to come from highest bliss
   Down to such a world as this!

6 Teach, O teach us, holy Child,
   By thy face so meek and mild,
   Teach us to resemble thee,
   In thy sweet humility:

                    Edward Caswall, 1814-78

34

LONDON WAITS

English Traditional Carol-Melody.
Setting from the Collection at
St. Patrick's Cathedral, Dublin

Ma - ry shall won - der, Ma - ry shall pon - der,

rall.

After both verses
Slow and soft

Ring out glad bells, ring out the sweet sto - ry.

58

SING a sweet song of Bethlehem city,
Carol to praise the Babe newly born;
Mary shall wonder, Mary shall ponder,
Angels shall sing this glad Christmas morn
Christ in his love, his love and his pity,
Stoops down to save poor sinners forlorn:

Ring out glad bells, ring out the sweet story.

2 Angels shall sing in glorious measures,
Shepherds shall haste and humbly draw near;
Mary shall wonder, Mary shall ponderᴗ
All that is told by prophet and seer.
Sages, bring gifts, and open your treasures,
Here is our hope: our Saviour is here:

C. E. Patton, 1855-1900

59

35

THE INFANT KING

From a Basque Noël.
Arr. by EDGAR PETTMAN, 1865-1943

Smoothly and not too fast

Sing lul-la-by.

p

p Sing lul-la-by.

p   SING lullaby!
Lullaby Baby, now reclining,
Sing lullaby!
Hush, do not wake the infant King.

mf   Angels are watching, stars are shining
Over the place where he is lying:
Sing lullaby.

2 Sing lullaby!
   Lullaby Baby, now a-sleeping,
   Sing lullaby!
   Hush, do not wake the infant King.
   Soon will come sorrow with the morning,
   Soon will come bitter grief and weeping:
   Sing lullaby.

   3 Sing lullaby!
   Lullaby Baby, now a-dozing,
   Sing lullaby!
   Hush, do not wake the infant King.
   Soon comes the Cross, the nails, the piercing,
dim.   Then in the grave at last reposing:
   Sing lullaby.

p   4 Sing lullaby!
   Lullaby! is the Babe a-waking?
   Sing lullaby!
   Hush do not stir the infant King.
f   Dreaming of Easter, gladsome morning,
   Conquering Death, its bondage breaking:
   Sing lullaby.

Sabine Baring-Gould, 1834-1924

36

LUTE-BOOK LULLABY

Melody from WILL BALLET'S
MS. Lute-Book, c. 1600,
in the Library of Trinity College, Dublin.
Har. by CHARLES WOOD, 1866-1926

Sweet was the song the Vir - gin sung When she, when she to Beth-lem Ju - da came, And was de - liv-er'd of a son, That bless-ed Je - sus hath to name.

Lul - la, lul - la, lul - la, lul-la-by, Lul - la, lul - la,

lul-la, lul-la-by, 'Sweet Babe,'— sung she, my

son, And eke a Sa-viour born, Who hast vouch-saf-ed from on

high To vis-it us that were for-lorn: La-lu-la,
high To vis-it us that were for-lorn: La-lu-la,
high To vis-it us

la-lu-la, la-lu-la-by. 'Sweet Babe', sung

And rocked him sweet-ly on her knee.
she, And rocked him sweet-ly on her knee.

*eke—also or moreover.

Will Ballet, 17th cent.

63

37

STILLE NACHT

Franz Xaver Grüber, *c.* 1787-1863

Smoothly, not too fast

Stille Nacht, heilige Nacht!

STILL the night, holy the night!
Sleeps the world, hid from sight;
Mary and Joseph in stable bare
Watch o'er the Child beloved and fair,
Sleeping in heavenly rest.

2 Still the night, holy the night!
Shepherds first saw the light,
Heard resounding clear and long,
Far and near, the angel-song,
'Christ the Redeemer is here.'

3 Still the night, holy the night!
Son of God, O how bright
Love is smiling from thy face!
Strikes for us now the hour of grace,
Saviour, since thou art born!

Joseph Mohr, 1792-1848
Tr. *Stopford A. Brooke*, 1832-1916

64

38

THE BABE IN BETHLEM'S MANGER English Traditional Carol-Melody.
Har. by MARTIN F. E. SHAW, 1875-1958

THE Babe in Bethlem's manger
　In humble form so low,　[laid,
By wondering angels is surveyed
　Through all his scenes of woe:

Nowell, Nowell, now sing a
　Saviour's birth;
All hail his coming down to earth
　Who raises us to Heaven.

2 For not to sit on David's throne
　With worldly pomp and joy;
He came to earth for sin t' atone,
　And Satan to destroy:

3 To preach the word of life divine,
　And feed with living bread,
To heal the sick with hand benign,
　And raise to life the dead:

4 He preached, he suffered, bled and
　Uplift 'twixt earth and skies; [died,
In sinners' stead was crucified,
　For sin a sacrifice:

5 Well may we sing a Saviour's birth,
　Who need the grace so given,
And hail his coming down to earth
　Who raises us to Heaven:

Traditional (English)

39

THE FIRST NOWELL

English Carol-Melody (altered) from
WILLIAM SANDYS' *Christmas Carols*, London, 1833.
Har. by SIR JOHN STAINER, 1840-1901

1. The first Now - ell the an - gel did say Was to
cer - tain poor shepherds in fields as they lay; In fields where
they lay keep-ing their sheep On a cold win-ter's night that
ff CHORUS
was so deep: Now - ell, Now - ell, Now - ell, Nowell, Born is the King of Is - ra - el.

66

2 They lookèd up and saw a star
   Shining in the east beyond them far,
   And to the earth it gave great light,
   And so it continued both day and night:

3 And by the light of that same star,
   Three wise men came from country far;
   To seek for a king was their intent,
   And to follow the star wherever it went:

4 This star drew nigh to the north-west,
   O'er Bethlehem it took its rest,
   And there it did both stop and stay
   Right over the place where Jesus lay:

5 Then entered in those wise men three,
   Most reverently upon their knee,
   And offered there in His presence,
   Both gold, and myrrh, and frankincense:

6 Then let us all with one accord
   Sing praises to our heavenly Lord,
   That hath made heaven and earth of nought,
   And with His blood mankind hath bought:

Traditional (*English*)

40

THE HOLLY AND THE IVY

English Traditional Carol-Melody.
Har. by GEORGE H. P. HEWSON, 1881-1972

THE holly and the ivy
  Now both are full well grown;
Of all the trees that are in the wood,
  The holly bears the crown:

  O the rising of the sun,
    And the running of the deer,
  The playing of the merry organ,
    Sweet singing in the quire.

2 The holly bears a blossom,
   As white as lily-flower;
   And Mary bore sweet Jesus Christ
   To be our sweet Saviour:

3 The holly bears a berry,
   As red as any blood;
   And Mary bore sweet Jesus Christ
   To do poor sinners good:

4 The holly bears a prickle,
   As sharp as any thorn;
   And Mary bore sweet Jesus Christ
   On Christmas Day in the morn:

5 The holly bears a bark,
   As bitter as any gall;
   And Mary bore sweet Jesus Christ
   For to redeem us all:

6 The holly and the ivy
   Now both are full well grown;
   Of all the trees that are in the wood,
   The holly bears the crown:

Traditional (*English*)

41

GEBORN IST UNS EIN KINDELEIN

Proper Melody (15th cent.)
from JOHANNES SPANGENBERG, 1484-1550,
as given by JOHANNES ZAHN, and
har. by Rev. G. R. WOODWARD, 1848-1934

Geborn ist uns ein Kindelein.

TO us is born a little Child
Of Mary, maiden-mother mild:
Yuletide a merry season is,
Babe Jesus our delight and bliss:

O Jesu, darling of my heart,
How rich in mercy, Babe, thou art!

2 Strange sight! Within a stable old,
  Lo! God is born in want and cold:
  O selfish world, this Babe, I say,
  Both put thee to the blush to-day:

3 The Child (so wide his mercies are)
  Peace, joy and bliss doth bring from far:
  Before his crib, in awe to him,
  Your faces veil, ye cherubim:

4 Now angels joyful hymns upraise,
  And God's own Son with carols praise:
  To Bethlehem the shepherds fare,
  And firstlings of their flock they bear:

5 With gladsome voice on Jesus call,
  Ye spirits of the righteous all:
  To-day is born Emmanuel—
  He make your souls at ease to dwell!

6 With Holy Ghost him praise above,
  Who gave his son, in tender love;
  And bless him for that lovely *May,
  Of whom the Lord was born to-day.

Köln Gesangbuch
Tr. *George R. Woodward*, 1848-1934

* May—maid

71

42

PUER NOBIS NASCITUR

Melody from
Piae Cantiones, Greifswald, 1582

2 Christ, from heav'n descending low,
  Comes on earth a stranger;
Ox and ass their owner know
  Becradled in a manger:
    Unto us, etc.

3 This did Herod sore affray,
   And grievously bewilder;
   So he gave the word to slay,
   And slew the little childer:
   Unto us, etc.

4 Of his love and mercy mild
   This the Christmas story;
   And O that Mary's gentle Child
   Might lead us up to glory!
   Unto us, etc.

5 We adore him A and O;
   [1]*Cum cantibus in choro,*
   Let our merry organ go,
   [2]*Benedicamus Domino.*
   Unto us, etc.

                              15th cent.
Tr. *George R. Woodward,* 1848-1934, and others

1 —With songs in chorus
2—Let us bless the Lord

43

KINGS OF ORIENT

John Henry Hopkins, jun., 1820-91

1. We three kings of O - ri - ent are; Bear-ing gifts we tra-verse a - far
5. Glo-rious now, be hold him a - rise, King, and God, and sa - cri-fice!

Field and foun-tain, moor and moun-tain, Fol-low-ing yon - der star:
Heaven sings Hal - le - lu - jah: Hal - le - lu-jah the earth re - plies:

REFRAIN *after each verse*

O star of won-der, star of night, Star with roy-al beau-ty bright; West-ward lead-ing, Still pro-ceed-ing, Guide us to thy per-fect light!

INTERLUDE

The kings
WE three kings of Orient are;
Bearing gifts we traverse afar
Field and fountain, moor and
Following yonder star: [mountain,

O star of wonder, star of night,
Star with royal beauty bright;
Westward leading, still proceeding,
Guide us to thy perfect light!

First king*
2 Born a King on Bethlehem plain,
Gold I bring to crown him again—
King for ever, ceasing never
Over us all to reign:

         * Melody only.

Second king*
3 Frankincense to offer have I;
Incense owns a Deity nigh:
Prayer and praising, all men raising,
Worship him, God most High:

Third king*
4 Myrrh is mine; its bitter perfume
Breathes a life of gathering gloom;
Sorrowing, sighing, bleeding, dying,
Sealed in the stone-cold tomb:

The kings
5 Glorious now, behold him arise,
King, and God, and sacrifice!
Heaven sings Hallelujah:
Hallelujah the earth replies:

John Henry Hopkins, jun., 1820-91

75

44

GREENSLEEVES

English Traditional Carol-Melody
from WILL BALLET's *MS. Lute-Book, c.* 1600,
in the Library of Trinity College, Dublin

WHAT child is this, who, laid to rest,
  On Mary's lap is sleeping?
Whom angels greet with anthems sweet,
  While shepherds watch are keeping?
This, this is the Christ the King,
  Whom shepherds guard and angels sing:
Haste, haste to bring him laud,
  The Babe, the son of Mary!

76

2 Why lies he in such mean estate,
    Where ox and ass are feeding?
  Good Christian, fear: for sinners hereᵕ
    The silent Word is pleading:
  Nails, spear, shall pierce him through,
    The Cross be borne, for me, for you:
  Hail, hail, the Word made flesh,
    The Babe, the son of Mary!

3 So bring him incense, gold, and myrrh,
    Come, peasant, king, to own him.
  The King of kings salvation brings:
    Let loving hearts enthrone him.
  Raise, raise the song on high!
    The Virgin sings her lullaby:
  Joy, joy, for Christ is born,
    The Babe, the son of Mary!

                    W. Chatterton Dix, 1837-98

45

WHEN THE CRIMSON SUN HAD SET
(LES ANGES DANS NOS CAMPAGNES)
(FIRST SETTING)

English form of a
French Traditional Carol-Melody.
Har. by CHARLES H. KITSON, 1874-1944

Briskly

Glo - - - - - - - - - - - - ri-a in ex-cel-sis De - o, Glo - - - - - - - - - - ri - a in ex-cel-sis De - - o.

WHEN the crimson sun had set,
  Sinking 'neath the frosty plain,
On a bright and cold midnight
  Broke the glad angelic strain:
    Gloria in excelsis Deo.

2 Shepherds, watching by their flocks,
    Upward look with wond'ring gaze,
  In the sky bright hosts espy,
    Filling all the heav'nly ways:

3 Hie they then in quick accord,
    Hasting to the manger-throne,
  Bending low with hearts aglow,
    God of God the Babe they own:

4 Joy with us, good Christian men,
    Christ is come to set us free;
  He was born on Christmas morn,
    Sing the glad Nativity:
    Anon., Edited by *J. A. Jennings*, 1855-1923

45

WHEN THE CRIMSON SUN HAD SET
(LES ANGES DANS NOS CAMPAGNES)
(SECOND SETTING)

Har. by
GEORGE H. P. HEWSON, 1881-1972

QUINTET UNACCOMPANIED
Five Parts (two Trebles)

CHORUS WITH ACCOMPANIMENT
slightly quicker

Glo — — — — — — — ri - a
in ex-cel-sis De - o, Glo — — —
— ri-a in ex-cel-sis De — o.—

WHEN the crimson sun had set,
　　Sinking 'neath the frosty plain,
On a bright and cold midnight
　　Broke the glad angelic strain:
　　　Gloria in excelsis Deo.

2 Shepherds, watching by their flocks,
　　Upward look with wond'ring gaze,
In the sky bright hosts espy,
　　Filling all the heav'nly ways:

3 Hie they then in quick accord,
　　Hasting to the manger-throne,
Bending low with hearts aglow,
　　God of God the Babe they own:

4 Joy with us, good Christian men,
　　Christ is come to set us free;
He was born on Christmas morn,
　　Sing the glad Nativity:

　　Anon., Edited by *J. A. Jennings*, 1855-1923

46
QUITTEZ, PASTEURS

French Carol-Melody

Lightly

God,__ the God__ who comes to take a - way your woe,__ The
God, the God who comes to take a - way your woe.

YE shepherds, leave your flocks upon the mountains,
Your hearths and homes and care of all your sheep:
O change your griefs for joy everlasting,
And haste ye to adoreᵕ
The God who comes to take away your woe.

2 Him shall ye find a-lying in the manger,
  An Infant weak in nakedness and cold.
  Behold and see his love beyond expressing
  In coming thus to you!
  In him the Saviour of mankind appears.

3 Ye kings, behold the star to you revealingᵕ
  The King of kings: your vows and homage pay.
  See where the Sun of righteousness arises
  On all the earth:
  To him your gold and myrrh and incense bring.

Quittez pasteurs
Tr. *W. A. Pickard-Cambridge*

47

WINCHESTER OLD   C.M.   Melody from
THOMAS EST's *Psalmes*, London, 1592

A - men.

WHILE shepherds watched their flocks by night,
All seated on the ground,
The angel of the Lord came down,
And glory shone around.

2 'Fear not,' said he; for mighty dread
Had seized their troubled mind;
'Glad tidings of great joy I bring
To you and all mankind.

3 'To you, in David's town, this day,
Is born of David's line
A Saviour, who is Christ the Lord;
And this shall be the sign:

4 'The heavenly Babe you there shall find
To human view displayed,
All meanly wrapped in swathing bands,
And in a manger laid.'

5 Thus spake the seraph; and forthwith
Appeared a shining throng
Of angels, praising God, who thus
Addressed their joyful song:

U 6 'All glory be to God on high,
And to the earth be peace;
Good-will, henceforth, from heaven to men
Begin, and never cease.'   Amen.

Nahum Tate, 1652-1715

INDEX OF FIRST LINES
(with tunes)